Walking with Dad

Written by Andrew Abel
Illustrations by Graeme Holding

Walking with Dad

Written by Andrew Abel

Illustrated by Graeme Holding

First Edition Jan 2023

ISBN 979-8-218-16174-3

memoriesfond.com

DEDICATION

From Andrew

To my sister, Catherine Clarke, in memory of our Dad

From Graeme

To my Dad, Sarah's Dad & Jo's Dad - Sensei

Walking with Dad
    down an old country lane.
Picking blackberries,
    with fingers fruit-stained.
Strolling through fields
    filled with root veg or grain.
Life moves us on,
    but the places remain.

Listening with Dad
    in the sun, wind or rain,
For the rooks, or an owl,
    or a faraway train.
Hearing him whistle
    a happy refrain.
We grow and we change,
    but the sounds are the same.

Reading with Dad
    bedtime stories again,
Of pirates and mermaids
    and dragons now slain.
Resting my head as
    sweet dreams fill my brain.
Drifting to sleep 'neath the
    warm counterpane.

Watching my Dad
    with a jig saw and plane.
Fashioning musicbox,
    castles, and games.
Smelling the wood
    as he follows the grain.
Carving his love
    into things that remain.

In the garden with Dad -
his treasured domain.
The scent of tomato plants
sweetly engrained.

With fruit trees and flowers,
   too many to name.
Marigold, Yellow Rose -
   summer again.

Climbing the hill over
    roughened terrain.
With the horse at the gate,
    we are stroking its mane.

Taking walks on the marsh
   as the day starts to wane.
Seeing furtive wild rabbits
   mid sunsets aflame.

Making memories fond

that will always remain.

ABOUT THE AUTHOR

Andrew Abel is originally from Helsby, Cheshire, England. He is now a software developer and lives in Silicon Valley, California with his wife, Angela. He developed a love of spoken rhyme from his grandfather, Wilfred Harrison, who loved to recite poems.

He is proud to be grandpa to Madison, Melia, Luke & Rocky.

Andrew Abel
andyabel@gmail.com
https://www.amazon.com/author/andrewabel

ABOUT THE ILLUSTRATOR

Graeme Holding's style of drawing is bright, fun and traditional but quirky. He likes to draw animals bringing a sense of personality to their characters. Graeme is from Helsby, Cheshire but now lives in Runcorn with his wife and four children.

After school and college he went on to complete a Children's book illustration course at the London Art College. Since then he has worked with publishers and private clients, producing illustrations for children's books.

Graeme Holding
graemeh@live.ca

·*Memories Fond*·

For more information see:

memoriesfond.com

For gifts and merchandise visit:

memoriesfond.etsy.com

Ingram Content Group UK Ltd.
Milton Keynes UK
UKHW021129210323
418862UK00003B/48